This book is dedicated to my family and especially Riley…my firstborn.

- Andra

www.mascotbooks.com

Doggy Drama

For more information, please contact:
Mascot Books
560 Herndon Parkway #120
Herndon, VA 20170
info@mascotbooks.com

Library of Congress Control Number: 2015908660

CPSIA Code: PRT0216B
ISBN-13: 978-1-63177-149-1

Printed in the United States

www.doggydrama.com
Contact the author: andra@doggydrama.com
Like us on Facebook: www.facebook.com/doggydrama

DOGGY DRAMA

written by Andra Gillum
illustrated by Andy Case

My name is Riley. I used to have a great life.

Mom and Dad brought me home when I was just a pup. For years, it was just the three of us. We played, took long walks, and I got lots of treats. It was all about me!

At Christmas, my stocking was stuffed full of tasty treats and squeaky Santas.

On Easter, my basket was filled with bunny-shaped bones.

On my birthday, they took me to Wendy's for a burger. (Even better than cake to a dog.)

The photo album was filled with darling pictures of me. We were all so happy, until one day…

Mom and Dad brought home a baby boy! (I wondered why Mom's belly was so huge.) They called him Max.

At first, all he did was CRY! There went my beauty sleep. It wasn't fair. He got to be loud, but I had to be quiet.

I even got in trouble for barking!
Hello...aren't dogs supposed to bark?

Then Max started to move. I wasn't expecting that one! He crawled everywhere, and started putting everything in his mouth.

Next he started to walk…and then run!
He chased me and grabbed my tail. *Yikes, Max…*
hands off the tail!

At Christmas, my stocking was only half full, but
you should have seen the size of Max's stocking!
Hello, Santa...hasn't Riley been a good girl?

After a while, I started to adjust. Max got more presents, but he did drop lots of food from his high chair. It was getting better until one day...

They brought home a baby girl!
Wasn't one kid enough? Her name was Mia.

At first, it was just more crying. But after a while, she started to move too! All these baby gates went up around the house. I was trapped! *Hello, Parents...Riley can't open gates!*

Mia liked to run and jump and play like Max, but she also liked to hug me, kiss me, and ride me around the room! *Hello, Mia...do I look like a horse?*

On Halloween, Mia got to wear the princess costume...not me!
Actually, that wasn't such a bad thing.

Now Mom's phone was filled with pictures of the kids. *Hello...where is Riley?*

Over the years, I learned to love the kids. They started school which freed up my days. More time to watch Animal Planet. Everything was pretty calm until one day...

Are you ready for this? They brought
home a new puppy! Her name was Lucy.
She was a smaller, less-cute version of me!

She cried all night long, just like the other two!
She chewed on everything and peed and
pooped in the house. So GROSS!

I did get extra treats while Lucy was being potty trained.
Big sister had to show her how it's done!

All she wanted to do was play, play, play. She'd throw her tail in my face, or bite at me, or run in circles just to get my attention. *Stop Lucy…You're making me dizzy!*

She got new chew toys, and delicious puppy food
that I wasn't allowed to touch. It was all about Lucy.
Lucy, Lucy, Lucy!

She follows me around all the time. I eat, she eats. I go outside, she goes outside. I go to my bed, she crowds into my bed. *Back off, Lucy...I need a little space!*

Each month, she calms down a bit. I suppose it's
nice to have some company every now and then.
Plus, when I mess up, she usually gets blamed.

The good old days are definitely gone, but I've learned to make it all work. Just don't tell my family. Who knows what they might bring home next! Meeeooooow!

The real Riley and Lucy
Hey, Lucy...scoot over!

ABOUT THE AUTHOR

Andra Gillum is a freelance writer and full-time mom. She lives in Columbus, Ohio with her husband, son, daughter, and two dogs.

Contact her at: andra@doggydrama.com
www.doggydrama.com